How to be a Ballerina

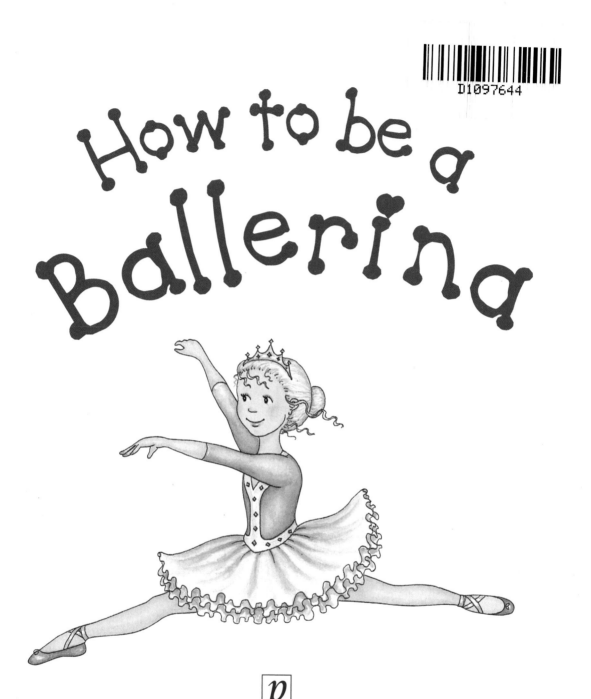

p

Written by Caroline Repchuk ◆ Illustrated by Fran Thatcher

Bella Ballerina

Bella looked around nervously at the other girls in her class. It was their first day at ballet school, and they were about to meet their teacher, the legendary Miss Meanie.

Rumor had it she gobbled up bad little ballerinas for breakfast. If they were going to keep on her good side, they'd have to stay on their toes!

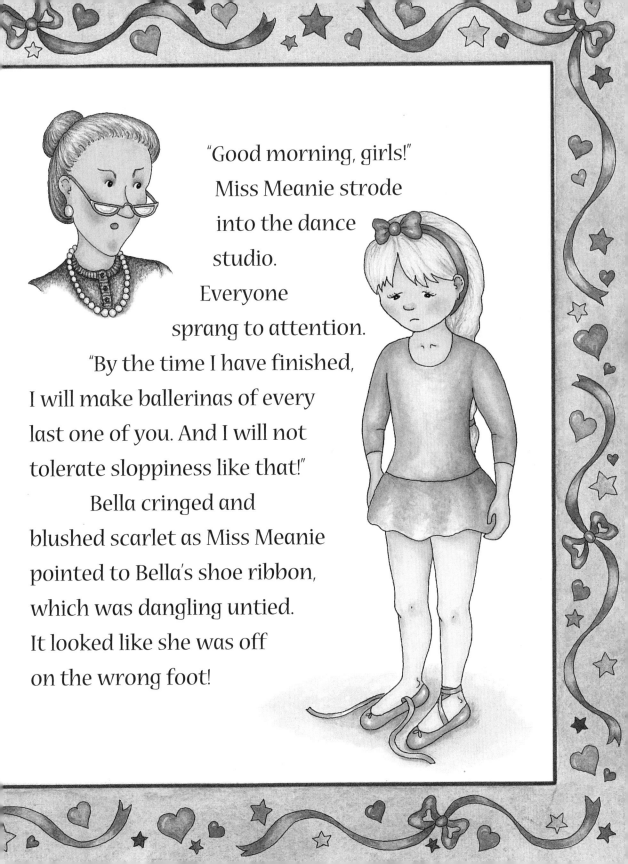

"Good morning, girls!"
Miss Meanie strode
into the dance
studio.
Everyone
sprang to attention.
"By the time I have finished,
I will make ballerinas of every
last one of you. And I will not
tolerate sloppiness like that!"
Bella cringed and
blushed scarlet as Miss Meanie
pointed to Bella's shoe ribbon,
which was dangling untied.
It looked like she was off
on the wrong foot!

Neat and Tidy

"I expect neatness and tidiness at all times. Hair up, jewelry off, smiles on!" ordered Miss Meanie. "Whether you're having fun, or not," she added.

Just in case anyone needed reminding, they ran through the proper way to tie shoe ribbons…

Preparing for Class

1. Keep your foot flat on the floor. Pass the inside ribbon across, around your ankle, and to the back again.

2. Cross the outside ribbon over the first one, and around your ankle.

3. Bring the ribbons together on the inside of your ankle and tie a knot.

4. Tuck in the ends neatly.

In a ballet class, your hair should always be tidy, and either put up in a bun, or pinned back securely. Jewelry has to be taken off, as it can get caught, scratch someone, or snag clothes.

Class Act

"Becoming a ballet dancer takes hard work, dedication, and discipline," declared Miss Meanie. "Which means paying attention in class, Bella!"

Bella, who had been watching the birds, quickly swung her head to face the front. Uh-oh—in trouble again!

Take Your Positions

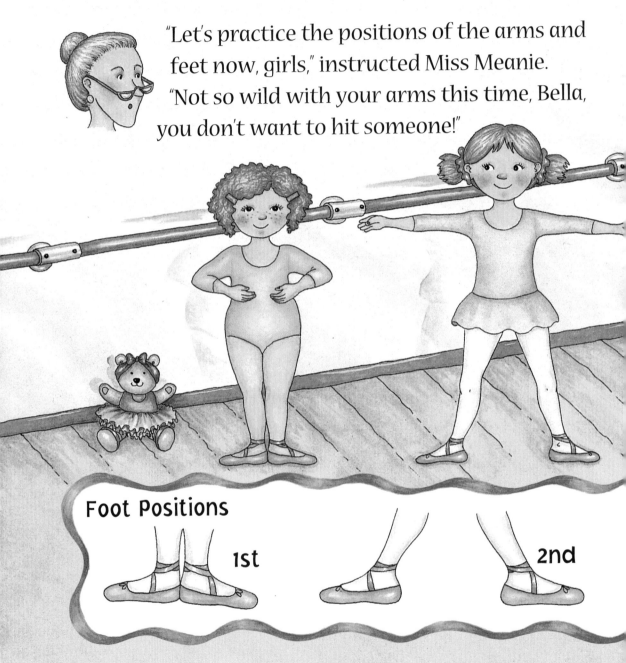

"Let's practice the positions of the arms and feet now, girls," instructed Miss Meanie. "Not so wild with your arms this time, Bella, you don't want to hit someone!"

Foot Positions

1st

2nd

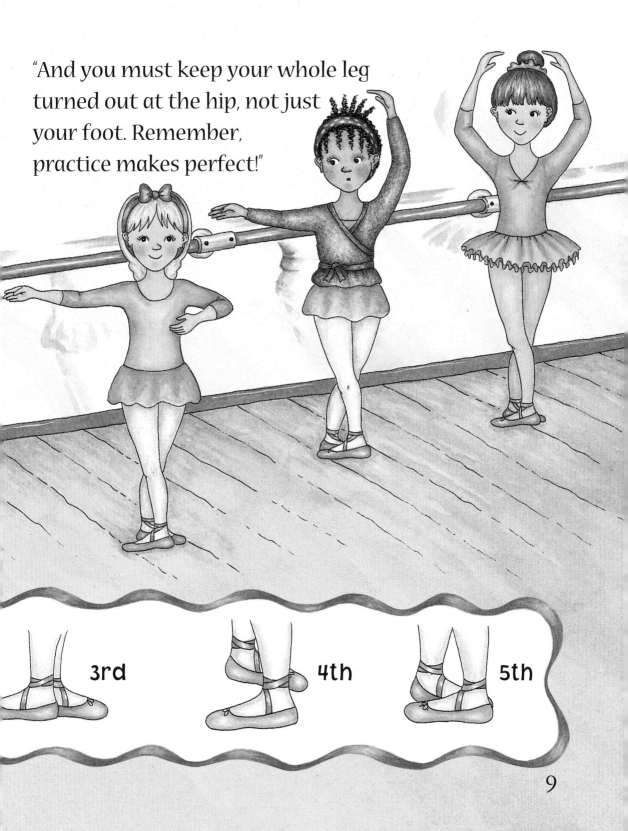

"And you must keep your whole leg turned out at the hip, not just your foot. Remember, practice makes perfect!"

3rd   4th   5th

9

Spinning Around

"Let's try some pirouettes now girls," said Miss Meanie. "You can go first, Bella."

Bella floated across the floor on the tip of her toes, feeling as light and delicate as a feather. She spun into a perfect pirouette— then crashed in a pile on the floor!

"Sorry Miss Meanie," she mumbled.

"I told you to keep your eye on something as you turned," said Miss Meanie.

"I did," said Bella, "I kept my eye on the cat, but he moved!"

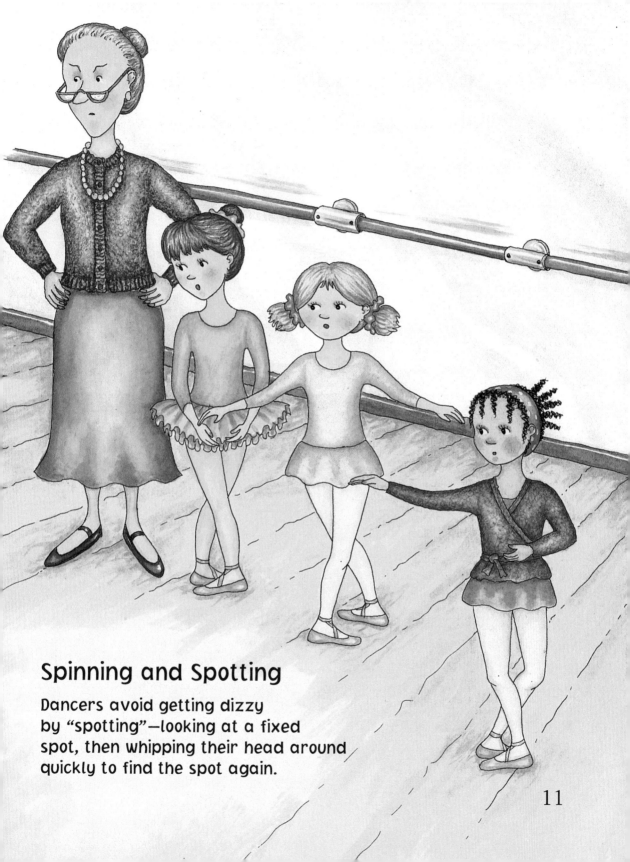

Spinning and Spotting

Dancers avoid getting dizzy
by "spotting"—looking at a fixed
spot, then whipping their head around
quickly to find the spot again.

11

Partner Work

"Partner work now!" said Miss Meanie. "Bella, you're with Boris." Bella waited with baited breath to meet her new partner.

Which of the tall, handsome boys would it be?

Then a short clumsy-looking boy stepped out from behind the others.

"Hello," he said. "I'm Boris." Bella's heart sank.

"A perfect match!" beamed Miss Meanie.

Without Words

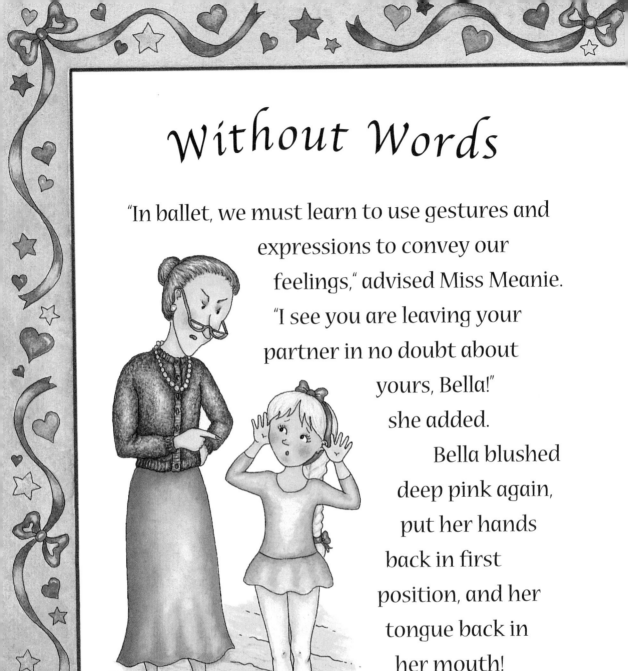

"In ballet, we must learn to use gestures and expressions to convey our feelings," advised Miss Meanie. "I see you are leaving your partner in no doubt about yours, Bella!" she added.

Bella blushed deep pink again, put her hands back in first position, and her tongue back in her mouth!

Telling the Story

Mime is an important part of ballet, and is used to convey feelings as well as the plot, especially in the older traditional ballets, such as "Swan Lake" and "The Sleeping Beauty." Each gesture has its own particular meaning:

Baby   **Beg**   **Sleep**   **Kill**

Fright   **Sorrow**   **Love**   **Hear**

The Sleeping Beauty

"Well, class, it's the moment you've all been waiting for!" announced Miss Meanie. "I am delighted to tell you that your first performance is to be the classic fairy tale ballet, "The Sleeping Beauty."

Prologue
The fairies bring gifts to the royal christening. Carabosse, the bad fairy, is angry at being left out, and casts a spell: Princess Aurora will prick her finger on a spindle and die.

Act 1
Princess Aurora pricks her finger on a spindle and collapses. The Lilac Fairy changes the spell so the princess is not dead, but in a deep sleep.

Act 2
Prince Florimund finds the castle and wakes Princess Aurora with a kiss.

Act 3
The wedding of Prince Florimund and Princess Aurora, with entertainment from Puss in Boots and the White Cat.

"This ballet has all the ingredients of a great fairy tale—a king and queen, good and bad fairies, a beautiful princess, and a brave, handsome prince," declared Miss Meanie.

Shall We Dance?

The class fell silent as Miss Meanie chose who would dance each part in the ballet.

"Bella and Boris, you are to dance the leading roles!" she announced. The pair looked at each other in horror and amazement!

"Yes, yes!" snapped Miss Meanie. "I know you are hardly star-crossed lovers, but despite that, you do actually dance very well together!"

18

The Sleeping Beauty

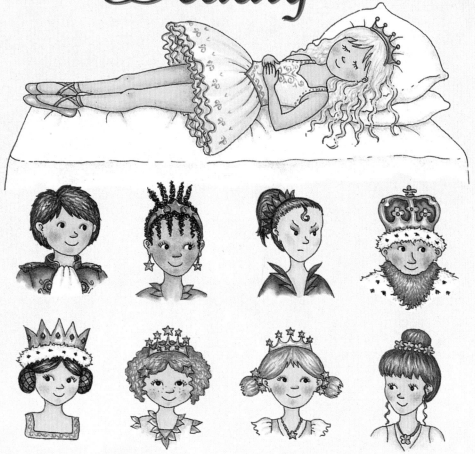

Curtain Up!

Finally opening night arrived.

"This is it," hissed Miss Meanie from the wings, giving the Lilac Fairy a nudge forward. "Make me proud!"

As the fairies twinkled across the stage, the magical fairy tale scene came to life.

In the Spotlight

Bella and Boris danced together beautifully. By the time Boris bent over to kiss his princess awake, they had won the hearts of their audience entirely.

Watching from the wings, Miss Meanie couldn't believe her eyes. Bella was finally a prima ballerina!

Ballet Words

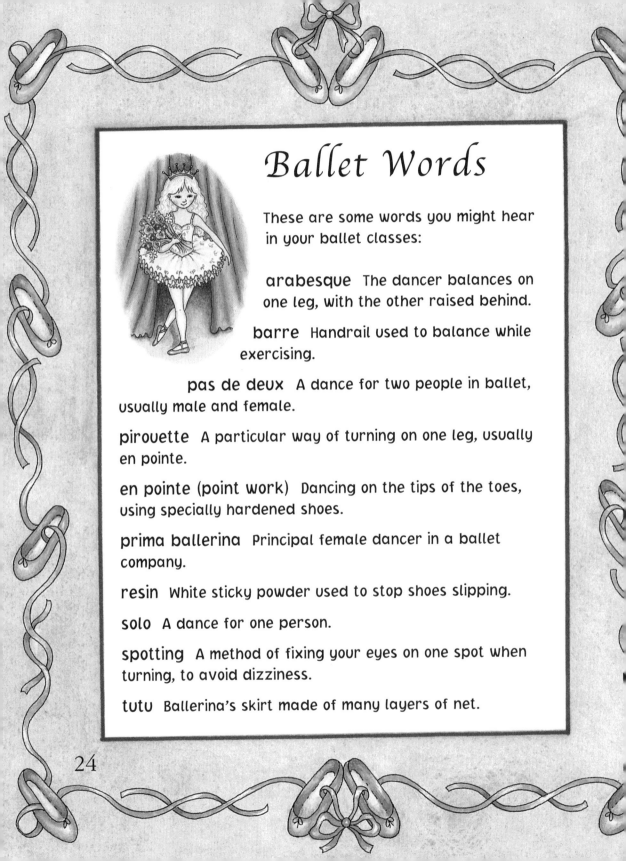

These are some words you might hear in your ballet classes:

arabesque The dancer balances on one leg, with the other raised behind.

barre Handrail used to balance while exercising.

pas de deux A dance for two people in ballet, usually male and female.

pirouette A particular way of turning on one leg, usually en pointe.

en pointe (point work) Dancing on the tips of the toes, using specially hardened shoes.

prima ballerina Principal female dancer in a ballet company.

resin White sticky powder used to stop shoes slipping.

solo A dance for one person.

spotting A method of fixing your eyes on one spot when turning, to avoid dizziness.

tutu Ballerina's skirt made of many layers of net.